Dear Parent and Educator,

Welcome to the Barron's Reader's Clubhouse, a series of books that provide a phonics approach to reading.

Phonics is the relationship between letters and sounds. It is a system that teaches children that letters have specific sounds. Level 1 books introduce the short-vowel sounds. Level 2 books progress to the long-vowel sounds. This progression matches how phonics is taught in many classrooms.

Luke's Mule introduces the long "u" sound. Simple words with this long-vowel sound are called **decodable words.** The child knows how to sound out these words because he or she has learned the sound they include. This story also contains **high-frequency words.** These are common, everyday words that the child learns to read by sight. High-frequency words help ensure fluency and comprehension. **Challenging words** go a little beyond the reading level. The child will identify these words with help from the illustration on the page. All words are listed by their category on page 24.

Here are some coaching and prompting statements you can use to help a young reader read *Luke's Mule:*

- **On page 4, "Luke" is a decodable word. Point to the word and say:**

  Read this word. How did you sound the word out? What sounds did it make?

  Note: There are many opportunities to repeat the above instruction throughout the book.

- **On page 11, "trade" is a challenging word. Point to the word and say:**

  Read this word. (Write *made* on a piece of paper, show it to the reader, and say:) *It rhymes with "made." How did you know the word? Did you look at the picture? How did it help?*

You'll find more coaching ideas on the Reader's Clubhouse Web site: *www.barronsclubhouse.com.* Reader's Clubhouse is designed to teach and reinforce reading skills in a fun way. We hope you enjoy helping children discover their love of reading!

Sincerely,

Nancy Harris

Nancy Harris
Reading Consultant

Luke has a brown mule.
His name is Duke.

Duke has a blue plume.

Sue likes the plume.

She puts the plume on
her hat.

You took Duke's plume.

That was rude.

I know. What can I do to make it up to you?

We can trade.

I will give you Duke's plume.

Will you give me your
blue cube?

It is too huge for Duke.

I know how Duke can use it.

Luke and Sue trade.

Sue looks cute in her
blue plume.

Duke looks fine in his new
blue cube.

Fun Facts About Mules

- A mule is a mix of a donkey and a horse.

- Have you ever heard the expression "stubborn as a mule"? Well, mules aren't really stubborn—they just won't put themselves in danger.

- Mules are very smart and will work hard. When they've had enough, however, they stop!

- The word *burro* means donkey in Spanish.

donkey

mule

horse

Make an "I'm Sorry" Card

The next time you and a friend have a fight or disagreement, make this card for your friend as a way to say "I'm sorry."

You will need:

- card stock or construction paper
- safety scissors
- markers or crayons
- googly eyes (optional)
- glue

1. Take the bottom right corner of a piece of card stock or construction paper. Bring it to the left edge of the paper to make a triangle. Press down on the fold.

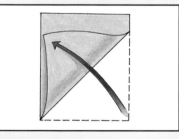

2. Cut off the excess paper on top of the triangle. (When you unfold your triangle, you should have a square.)

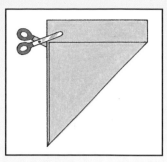

3. Hold the triangle so that the folded side is on top and the open point is at the bottom. Fold over the edges of the remaining points to make the dog's ears.

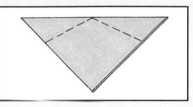

4. Put a face on your dog using the googly eyes and markers or crayons. On the back of the card, you can write "I'm sorry" . . . or any kind of a note to a friend.

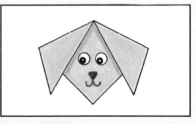

Word List

Challenging Words	trade		
Long U Decodable Words	blue cube cute Duke Duke's huge Luke mule plume	rude Sue use	
High-Frequency Words	a and brown can do for give has her his how I in	is it know likes looks me new on puts she that the too	took was what you your